THOMAS & FRIENDS ™

This annual belongs to:

....

Age:

....

THOMAS & FRIENDS ™

ANNUAL 2020

EGMONT
We bring stories to life

First published in Great Britain in 2019 by Egmont UK Limited
The Yellow Building, 1 Nicholas Road, London W11 4AN

Written by Laura Jackson
Designed by Martin Aggett

 Thomas the Tank Engine & Friends™

CREATED BY BRITT ALLCROFT

ISBN 978 1 4052 9447 8
70377/001

Printed in Italy

CONTENTS

Meet the Sodor Steam Team 8

Big World Rail Trail 10

Snowy Spot 12

All About Percy 14

Guess with Percy 15

Story – The Animal Ark **16**

Count Along 22

Really Wild Art 23

All About Nia 24

Misty Maze 25

Animal Friends 26

Memory Quiz 27

Colour Splash 28

Twisty Tracks 29

All About James 30

Splendid Red **31**

Story – Thomas in the Wild **32**

Journey through China 38

All About Rebecca 40

Very Important Cargo 41

Naughty Trucks! 42

Night-time Shadows 43

Grumpy Gordon 44

Engine Numbers 45

Adventure Mobile 46

Posters 49

Flying High 51

Jigsaw Jumble 52

3, 2, 1 ... Race! 53

Colour, Spot and Learn 54

Sodor Quiz 56

What's the Time? 58

Story – Kangaroo Christmas . . . **60**

Hop to It! 64

Nia Close-ups 65

Being Kind with the Steam Team! . . 67

Answers 68

MEET THE SODOR STEAM TEAM

When there's a job to do on Sodor, the Steam Team is on its way.

I'm the Number 1 blue engine!

HERE COMES THOMAS!

He may be small, but Thomas is one of the bravest and friendliest engines on Sodor.

I am a Really Splendid Engine.

HERE COMES JAMES!

James brings fun wherever he goes, even though he is a big show-off!

Mail coming through!

HERE COMES PERCY!

Percy's favourite job is to pull the Mail Train, and always with a smile.

Yay, me!

Excellent Emily can do it!

HERE COMES EMILY!

Cheerful and confident, Emily loves telling the other engines what to do.

HERE COMES REBECCA!

Rebecca is one of the biggest and strongest engines on Sodor, but she has lots of accidents!

I am the strongest! I am the best!

We're a good team!

HERE COMES NIA!

Nia is very clever and loves helping her friends to solve problems.

HERE COMES GORDON!

Gordon is very proud to pull the mighty Express.

BIG WORLD RAIL TRAIL

Hop on board!

Use your finger to follow the tracks and join Thomas on his big adventures around the world.

Hello, I'm Shane!

WELCOME TO AUSTRALIA

Boing! How many kangaroos can you count?

WELCOME TO INDIA

Hello, I'm Ashima!

What sound does a monkey make?

SNOWY SPOT

The engines are watching the snow falling! Can you spot five differences in the second picture?

1

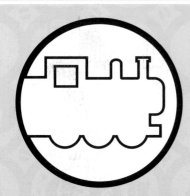

Colour in a badge, each time you find a difference.

Answers on page 68.

ALL ABOUT PERCY

Percy is a fun, little engine who is happy chuffing around Sodor, but he loves to hear all about his best friend Thomas' big adventures!

Shiny, gold dome

Bright green paintwork

Only teasing!

Strong buffers

NO 6

FAST FACT
Percy also works at the mine, so he is often the dirtiest engine in the sheds!

Point to Percy's number 6

GUESS WITH PERCY

Can you help Percy solve these puzzles?

Point to the **TALLEST** animal.

Point to the **SMALLEST** animal.

Point to the **SHOCKED** face.

Point to the **RED** engine.

15

Answers on page 68.

THE ANIMAL ARK ▶▶

It was a cold, snowy day on Sodor. Thomas had slid to a stop outside the Animal Park where Jack, the Head Keeper, was looking worried.

"The boiler in the winter house has broken," Jack told Thomas. "We need it to keep the animals warm. Emily was meant to be collecting a new boiler from the docks..."

"I'm on my way there right now!" said Thomas. *"I'll find out what's happened."*

When Thomas pulled up at Brendam Docks, Emily told him there was no sign of the boiler anywhere.

"It's the bad weather," said Carly.

"I don't think it'll be here for days."

"But those animals need to be kept warm, now!"
said Thomas, alarmed.
He **whooshed** off down the track to find The Fat Controller. This was an emergency!

At Knapford Station, The Fat Controller, Percy and Henry were all shocked to hear Thomas' news.

"Dear, oh dear," said The Fat Controller. "Now, where's the hottest place on Sodor ... the Steamworks! Thomas, grab some trucks and take the animals there right away."

In no time at all, Thomas was back at the Animal Park ready to collect the animals. One by one, the animals boarded the trucks.

Giraffes, elephants, camels, monkeys, ostriches – Thomas had never transported so many animals before!

TOOT! TOOT!

Thomas whistled happily, as he set off into the snow. But he hadn't gone far, when he came to a stop.

SCREEEEECCCHHHH!

The tunnel ahead was snowed in. Quickly backing up along the track, Thomas needed to find another route – and fast. The animals were getting cold.

CLICKERTY-CLACK   CLICKERTY-CLACK   CLICKERTY-CLACK   CLICKERTY-CLACK

Thomas was soon on the move again, but the ice on the tracks was slippery.

When he came down Brandon Hill, his wheels started to slip. He was going ...

FASTER FASTER FASTER

He tried to brake, but it was no use ...

CRASH!

Thomas bashed straight into a snowdrift. Oh dear, the animals were very cold, and now Thomas was completely stuck.

One of the elephants let out a mighty **HARUMPH!** This gave Thomas an amazing idea. When he crashed in India, elephants had pushed him back onto the track ...

Sure enough, when Jack let the elephants out, they started to **push ...** and **push ...** and **push ...** until the trucks jolted forward. Thomas and the animals were back on track!

It was starting to get dark, and the animals were shivering. Thomas knew there wasn't enough time to get to the Steamworks now. There was only one place to go ...

... Tidmouth Sheds!

The engines couldn't believe their eyes when they saw Thomas and the animals.

"Our boilers will keep them nice and warm," Thomas told his friends.

"Animals?" gasped Gordon. **"Oh, the indignity!"**

But Thomas felt very proud and happy to be helping the animals – even if it did mean the engines didn't get much sleep all night!

COUNT ALONG

Thomas loves meeting wild animals all over the world. Help him count up the giraffes, the elephants and the tigers.

When you have counted them, point to the answers in the number line below.

1 2 3 4 5 6 7 8 9 10

Answers on page 68.

REALLY WILD ART

Grab your best pencils and draw some animals you would love to see in the wild.

ALL ABOUT NIA

Kind, colourful and friendly, Nia moved to Sodor from Kenya. A new member of the Steam Team, she brings adventure wherever she goes.

Nº18

Lamp

Bright, colourful patterns

Two engines are better than one!

Brake pipe

FAST FACT

Thomas' coaches, Annie and Clarabel, taught Nia how to read numbers.

What colours can you spot on Nia?

MISTY MAZE

It is a misty morning in the savannah and Nia can't find her way. Guide her safely along the track.

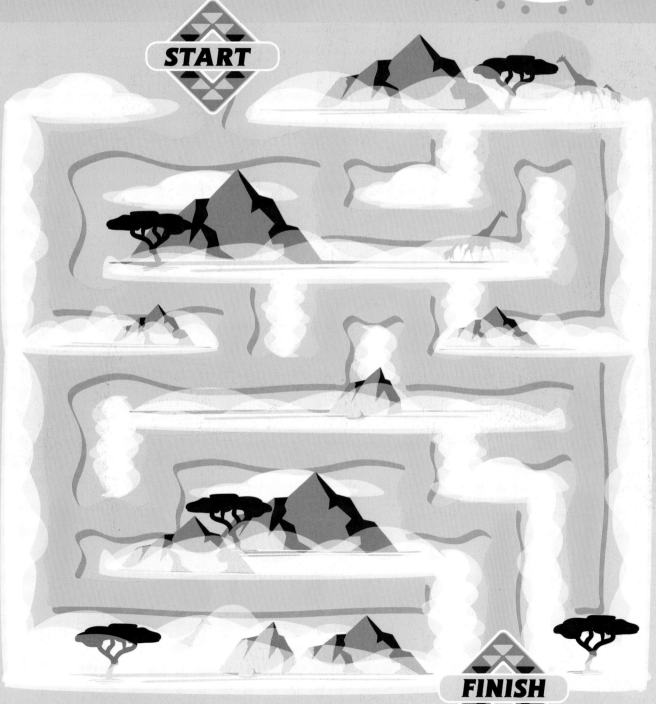

START

FINISH

Answers on page 68.

ANIMAL FRIENDS

Follow the lines to find out which animals the engines meet on their travels.

1

2

3

a

b

c

Answers on page 68.

MEMORY QUIZ

Look at this picture of Thomas carefully. Then cover it up with a piece of paper and see how much you can remember.

1 Which animals are jumping on Thomas?

2 What does Thomas have on top of his funnel?

3 Is there another engine in the picture?

4 Is the driver climbing a tree?

5 Is it day or night?

Answers on page 68.

COLOUR SPLASH

The engines are lining up for a new paint job. Draw lines to match up each engine with the correct paint colour.

ROSIE THOMAS NIA PERCY

Orange

Green

Red

Blue

Answers on page 68

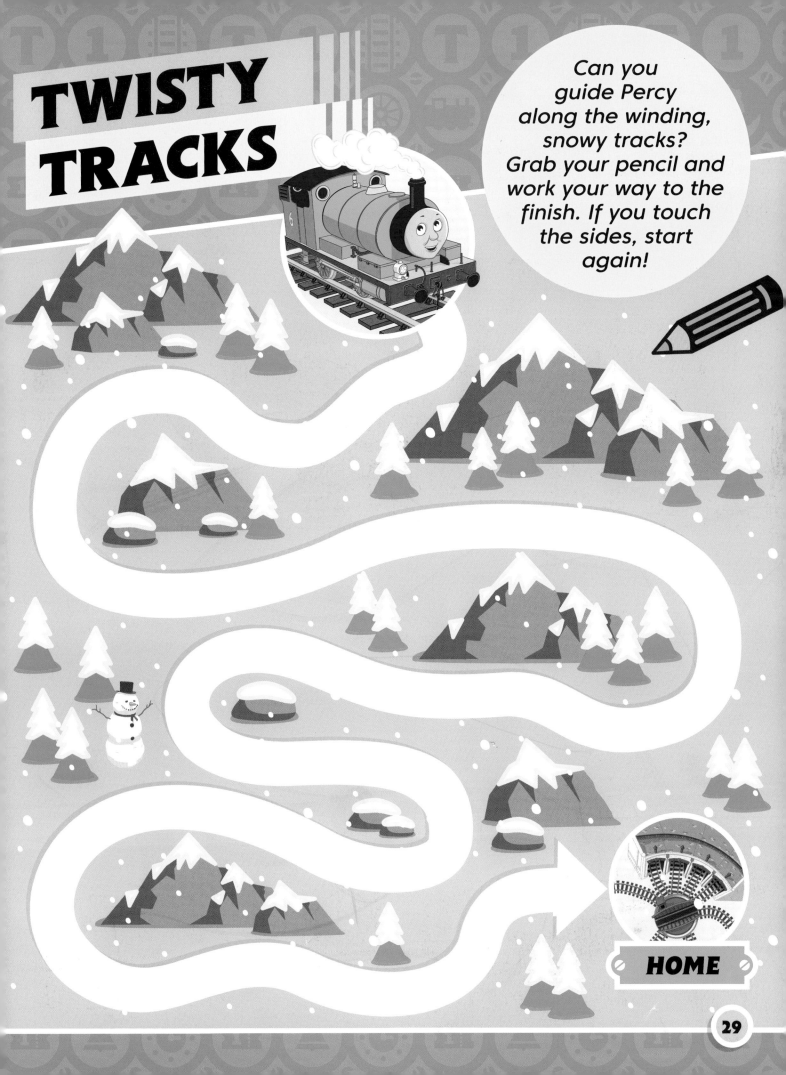

TWISTY TRACKS

Can you guide Percy along the winding, snowy tracks? Grab your pencil and work your way to the finish. If you touch the sides, start again!

HOME

ALL ABOUT JAMES

James may show off about his red paintwork, but he has lots of friends on Sodor. His worst job is pulling the Troublesome Trucks – they make him very cross

Black funnel

Cab

Smoke box

Mind my shiny paintwork!

FAST FACT
James hates getting dirty.
Clean is best for this splendid engine!

No5

What colour is James' dome?

SPLENDID RED ||||

Make James proud by using your best red crayons to make his paintwork shine.

THOMAS IN THE WILD ▶▶

The sun was rising over the Chinese Railway, and Thomas and Yong Bao were on their way to work.

Thomas was very excited, because today he was taking a crew to the Nature Reserve to film giant pandas.

"The giant panda is the national animal of China," explained Yong Bao. **"They are very rare."**

Thomas' coaches, Yin-Long and An-An were just as excited as Thomas. **"They are super cute!"** said An-An.

As Thomas pulled into the station to pick up the crew, he kept thinking about seeing a **giant panda**.

"Trains can't go inside the reserve," said Yin-Long. "You won't see one, Thomas,"

Thomas frowned. "Well, I'll see one in the forest on the way then."

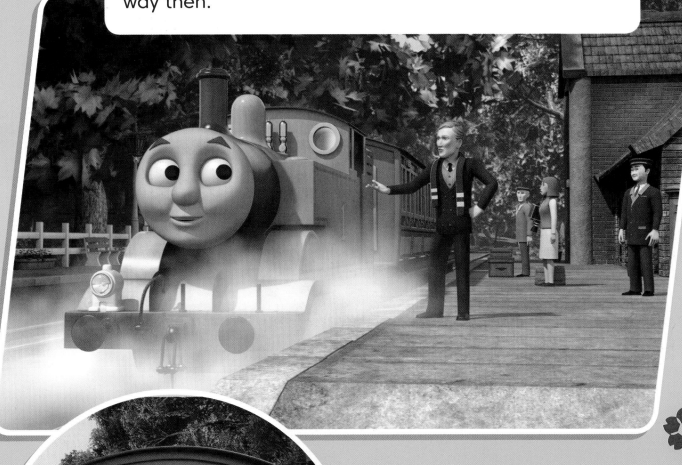

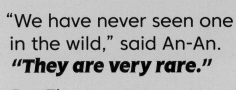

"We have never seen one in the wild," said An-An. ***"They are very rare."***

But Thomas was determined. He was sure he could find a giant panda!

Toot! Toot! Thomas whistled along the tracks, looking in the forest for the pandas. Suddenly, he shuddered to a stop.

screeeeech!
"Fizzling fireboxes! I can see something in the trees," said Thomas.

Sure enough, there was something in the trees. But it was a red panda.

"They are rare, too," said Yin-Long. "But not as rare as the giant panda. You're not going to find one, Thomas."

The more the coaches told Thomas he wouldn't find one, the more determined Thomas became.

Further along the track, Thomas heard a rustling in the bamboo.

"I can see something!"
Thomas whispered. "It's black and white. Is it a ... giant panda?"

"No, Thomas," said An-An. "That's an Asian black bear. They are quite rare ..."

"... but not as rare as a giant panda,"
puffed Thomas, feeling disappointed.

As they got closer to the Nature Reserve, Thomas started to worry that maybe he wouldn't find one.

He chuffed and puffed slowly along the track.

"Hurry up, Thomas!" said the coaches.

But Thomas would not speed up. He was too busy looking through bamboo. He had spotted something black and white and furry ...

"Are they ...?" Thomas started.

"They are!" gasped An-An.

Two giant pandas crept out from behind a tree! They were much smaller than Thomas had imagined.

"They are cubs," said An-An.
"Look, there's the mother!"

Thomas was so pleased he had found not one giant panda, but three! Thomas, An-An and Yin-Long kept completely silent as they watched the amazing animals.

"I can't believe we have seen a giant panda in the wild," whispered Yin-Lang.
"All because of you, Thomas."

"You didn't give up until we had seen one," smiled An-An.

With one last glance at the pandas, Thomas puffed away happily, feeling very proud that he hadn't given up.

Peep! Peep!

JOURNEY THROUGH CHINA

Guide Thomas through the Chinese Railway, passing all the amazing animals and new friends along the way. Each time you pass an animal or a friend, shout out, **"Toot! Toot!"**

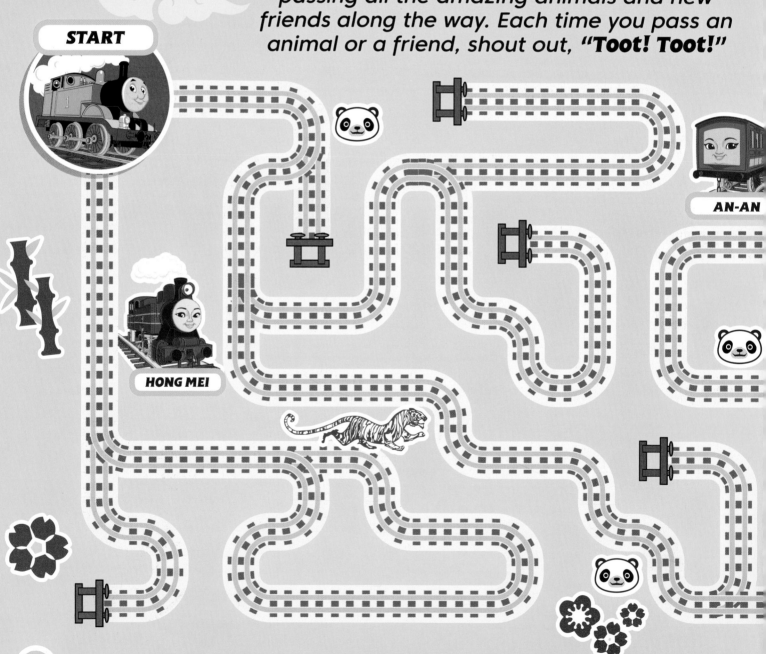

START

HONG MEI

AN-AN

YONG BOA

LEI

YIN-LONG

I travelled with Thomas!

ALL ABOUT REBECCA

Fast, fun and a little bit clumsy, Rebecca is built for speed. If only she knew how strong she was, she might not have so many accidents – whoops!

Yellow boiler

Metal wheels with yellow paint

Oops, sorry!

№22

Coupling hook

FAST FACT
Along with Gordon, it's Rebecca's job to pull the Express.

Does Rebecca look happy or sad?

VERY IMPORTANT CARGO

Rebecca loves to pull cargo all over Sodor. Pile up the flatbeds by drawing exciting things for Rebecca to deliver.

NIGHT-TIME SHADOWS

It's hard to work out who is who in the dark! Draw lines to match the shadow to the friend.

Rosie

Cranky

Emily

Bertie

a

b

c

d

Answers on page 68

GRUMPY GORDON

Oh dear, Gordon is not having a good day! Can you spot the odd picture out?

1

2

3

4

5

6

Answers on page 68

ENGINE NUMBERS

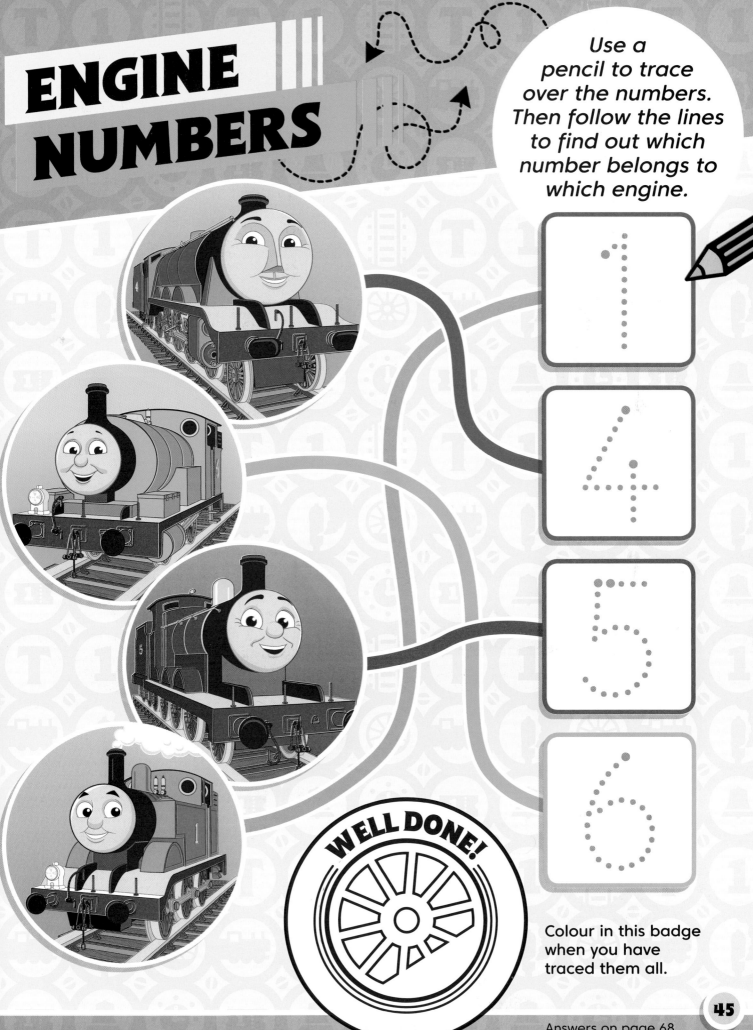

Use a pencil to trace over the numbers. Then follow the lines to find out which number belongs to which engine.

1

4

5

6

WELL DONE!

Colour in this badge when you have traced them all.

45

Answers on page 68

ADVENTURE MOBILE

Follow these instructions to make an adventure mobile for your bedroom.

You will need:

★ your animal and engine pieces

★ scissors

★ crayons

★ string or thread

★ sticky tape

★ two wooden dowels (if you don't have these to hand, you could use two pencils or sticks)

How to make:

★ Use your crayons to colour your animal and engine pieces.

★ Ask an adult to cut out your pieces and punch out the holes at the top of each.

★ Make a cross shape with the two dowels (or pencils). Use a long piece of string or thread to tie them tightly in the middle.

★ Cut five more lengths of string or thread. Tie one in the centre of your cross, and four others at the ends.

★ Feed the other end of the thread through the holes in your animal and train pieces. Use sticky tape to fix the thread to the back of the pieces.

Now it is ready to hang from your ceiling!

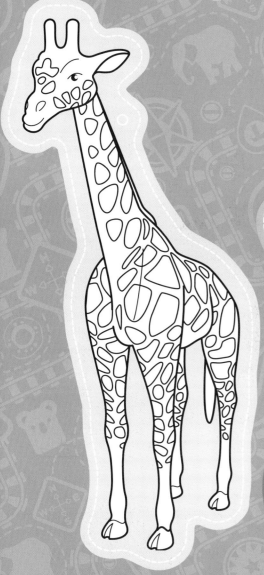

Ask a grown-up to help you when using scissors.

Ask a grown-up to help you when using scissors.

THE STEAM TEAM

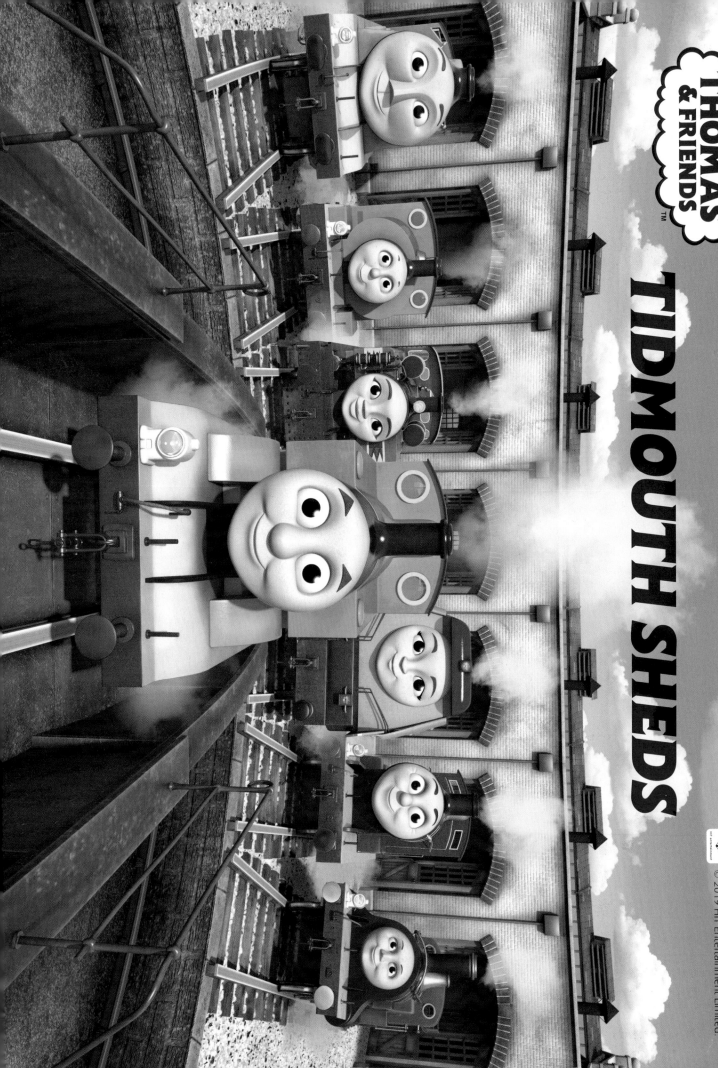

TIDMOUTH SHEDS

FLYING HIGH

Join the dots to finish Harold whizzing through the sky. Draw some clouds and a big sunshine, too.

SODOR AIRPORT

JIGSAW JUMBLE

Thomas and Rebecca are on the move! Which jigsaw piece is missing from this picture?

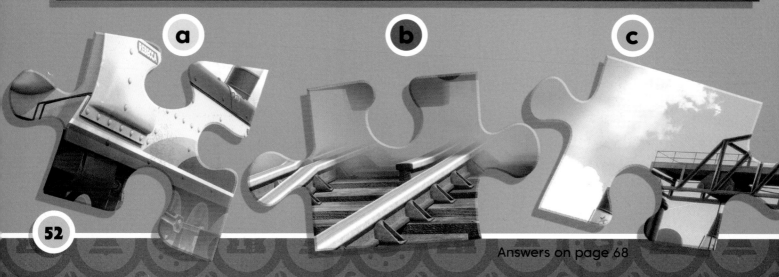

Answers on page 68

3, 2, 1...
RACE!

Challenge a friend to race around Sodor. Decide who is Rebecca and who is Gordon, grab a pencil and race each other to the finish.

Gordon

Rebecca

Colour the winner's badge if you come first.

WINNER!

53

COLOUR, SPOT AND LEARN

Nia wants to show you some of the amazing animals in Africa. Take the challenges in the panel to play along.

How many giraffes can you count?

Point to two animals that can fly.

Point to the animal with a big, long trunk.

Can you spot an animal that makes a **ROAR** sound?

Use your brightest crayons to colour in Nia.

Answers on page 68

DID YOU KNOW?
Elephants love to swim and squirt water. **SPLASH!**

DID YOU KNOW?
Giraffes are the tallest land animals in the world.

SODOR QUIZ

The Fat Controller knows everything about the Island of Sodor. Take his test to show him how much you know, too.

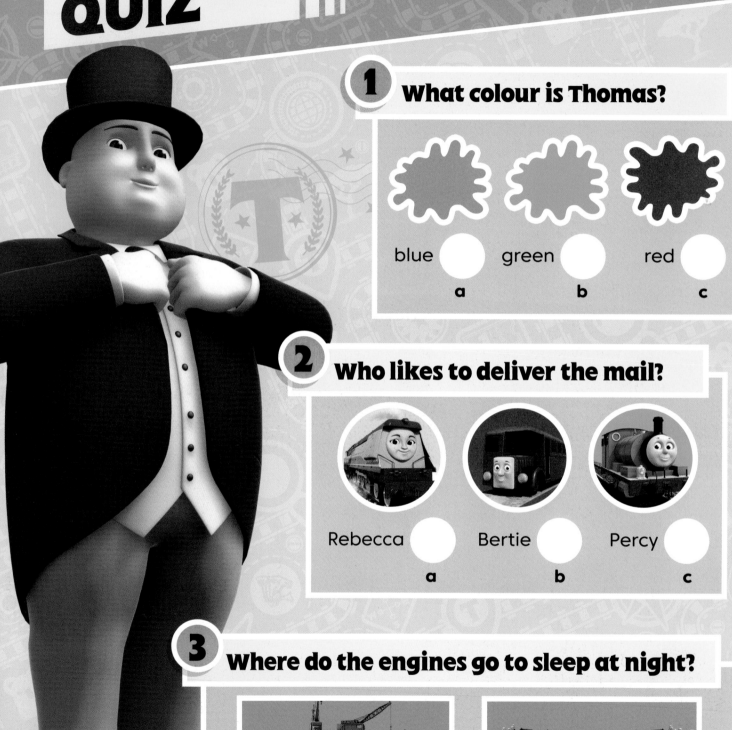

1 **What colour is Thomas?**

blue ⚪   green ⚪   red ⚪

    a   b   c

2 **Who likes to deliver the mail?**

Rebecca ⚪   Bertie ⚪   Percy ⚪

    a   b   c

3 **Where do the engines go to sleep at night?**

Brendam Docks ⚪   Tidmouth Sheds ⚪

    a   b

Check the answers on page 68 and then see how you scored.

4 ## Who is Percy's best friend?

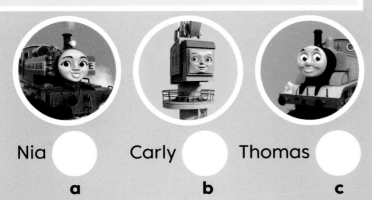

Nia a

Carly b

Thomas c

5 ## What do the engines do at a red signal?

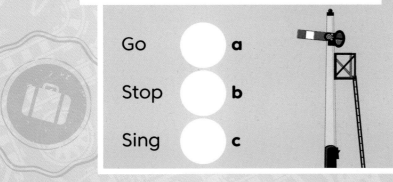

Go a

Stop b

Sing c

6 ## What number is Thomas?

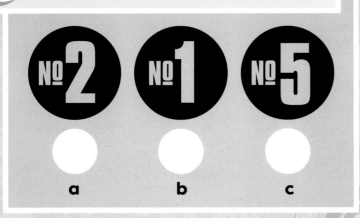

№2 a

№1 b

№5 c

1-2 **Well done for trying.** You can help Percy deliver the mail.

3-4 **Amazing work.** You can join the Search and Rescue team.

5-6 **You are a Very Useful Engine!** You can lead the Steam Team!

57

WHAT'S THE TIME?

Trace over the clocks and find out all about Thomas' very busy day.

Tick, tock, tick, tock ...

7 o'clock
Good morning, Thomas! It's time to leave Tidmouth Sheds.

8 o'clock
First stop, *Brendam Docks* to pick up cargo from Cranky.

11 o'clock
Thomas and Bertie have a race. *Whoosh!*

2 o'clock
Thomas to the **rescue** at the quarry!

4 o'clock
It's snowing!
Thomas is carrying a very important load.

6 o'clock
Phew! Thomas drops off presents for the Christmas party, just in time.

8 o'clock
What a busy day! *Goodnight, Thomas.*

KANGAROO CHRISTMAS

Listen to the story about Thomas in Australia. When you see a picture, join in and say the word!

kangaroo	girl	snow	sun	Thomas

It was Christmas Day, and was in Australia. In

Sodor, Christmas Day is always full of . In Australia,

the was very hot. missed the , and he

felt sad as he pulled into Pine Creek Station.

A little put her new toy on to Thomas' buffer.

Suddenly, a real mother hopped onto the

platform – and put the toy into her pouch! **"No!"**

said the little . But the mother had already

bounced away, taking the toy with her!

"I'll get your toy back!" said to the little .

The mother had leaped right over a steep creek

and bounced away into the outback. "I'll never find her

now," sighed .

Further down the line, spotted a baby

by the tracks, all alone. 'That must be the mother

kangaroo's baby!' thought . And sure enough, the

mother appeared and hopped over to the baby.

She threw the toy  onto the ground, and safely

put her baby into her pouch. All the passengers

cheered, and the little was so happy to have her

toy back. smiled as he watched the

hug her parents. "Christmas isn't about or

presents, and it doesn't matter if the shines!

It is about being with family and friends." **Toot! Toot!**

HOP TO IT!

START

The kangaroos are lost, and a bushfire is on its way! Quickly guide Thomas through the outback to collect up all of the kangaroos safely.

YOU DID IT!

Colour in the badge when you have finished.

NIA CLOSE-UPS

Nia is collecting some funny passengers today! Tick the close-ups when you find them in the big picture.

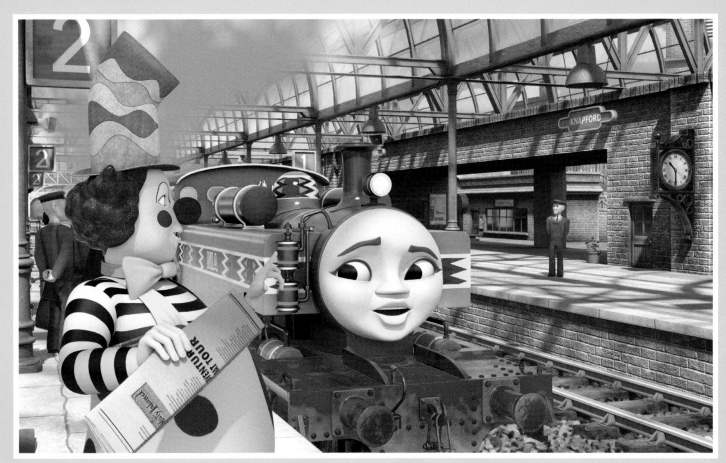

BEING KIND WIT THE STEAM TEAM!

Can you do something kind every day? As you do the challenges colour in the stars and when you get to the end, fill in Thomas' Very Important certificate.

I made something for a friend.

I shared my toys.

I tidied my room.

I helped to make a meal.

I cheered somebody up.

I made somebody happy.

I tried my best.

BEING KIND CERTIFICATE

This is to certify that

....

has been kind with the Steam Team!
You are a Very Important friend.

From,
Thomas

ANSWERS

Pages 10-11
BIG WORLD RAIL TRAIL
a. 4 kangaroos
b. Ooh-ooh-ooh!
c. A dragon face
d. 2 eagles

Pages 12-13
SNOWY SPOT

Page 15
GUESS WITH PERCY

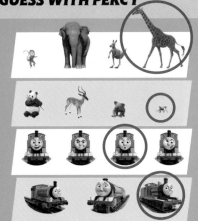

Page 22
COUNT ALONG
4 giraffes
3 elephants
6 tigers

Page 25
MISTY MAZE

Page 26
ANIMAL FRIENDS
1. b
2. c
3. a

Page 27
MEMORY QUIZ
1. Monkeys
2. A crown
3. No
4. No
5. Day

Page 28
COLOUR SPLASH
Rosie - Red
Thomas - Blue
Nia - Orange
Percy - Green

Pages 38-39
JOURNEY THROUGH CHINA

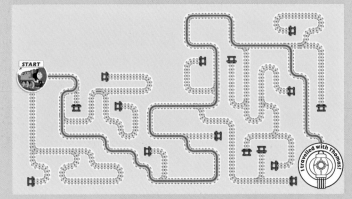

Page 42
NAUGHTY TRUCKS!
1. Gordon   2. Rebecca
3. James   4. Thomas

Page 43
NIGHT-TIME SHADOWS
a. Emily
b. Bertie
c. Cranky
d. Rosie

Page 44
GRUMPY GORDON
4. is the odd picture out

Page 45
NUMBER MIX-UP
1. is Thomas
4. is Gordon
5. is James
6. is Percy

Page 52
JIGSAW JUMBLE
a. is the missing piece

Page 54
COLOUR, SPOT AND LEARN
3 giraffes
The lion roars

Page 56
SODOR QUIZ

1	2	3	4	5	6
a	c	b	c	b	b

Page 64
HOP TO IT!

Page 65
NIA CLOSE-UPS